Contents

AGES 4–5
PRE-SCHOOL

Sorting

You can sort objects by putting them into **sets**.

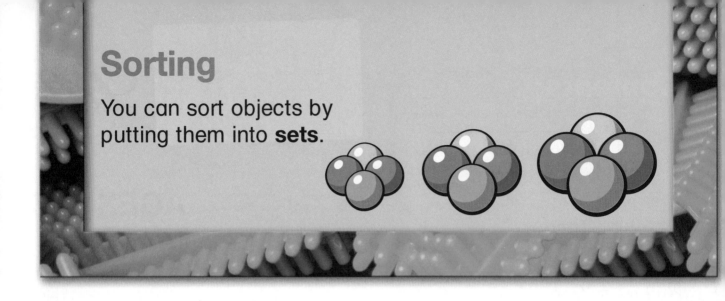

I **Sort these in different ways.**

a Find a set of forks.

b Find a set of red things.

c Find a set of small things.

d Find a set of knives.

II **Where do these objects belong? Draw lines to join each one to the correct room.**

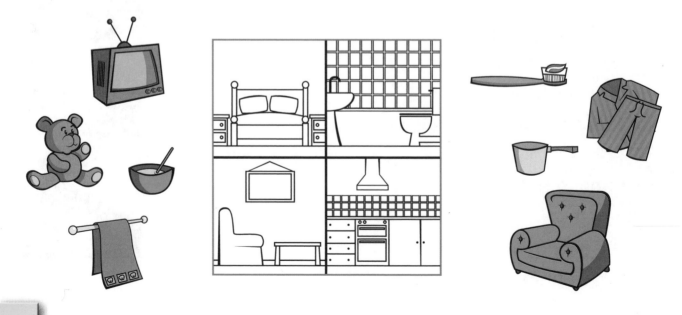

Matching pairs

A pair of objects is a set of two things.

Sometimes pairs match – they may **look the same**.

Sometimes pairs **go together**.

 Draw lines to join the matching pairs of shoes.

 Which pairs go together? Fill them in with the same colour.

3

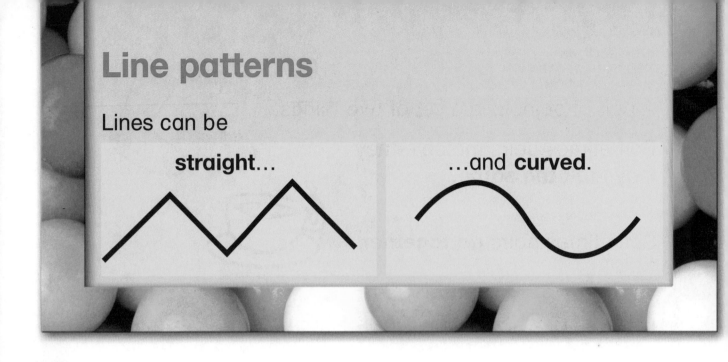

Line patterns

Lines can be

straight...

...and curved.

I Draw over these lines.

a

b

c

d

e

f

g

h

II Design your own line pattern. Draw it as a border for this picture.

Matching shapes

Look at the shapes of objects around you.

See what makes them the **same** and what makes them **different**.

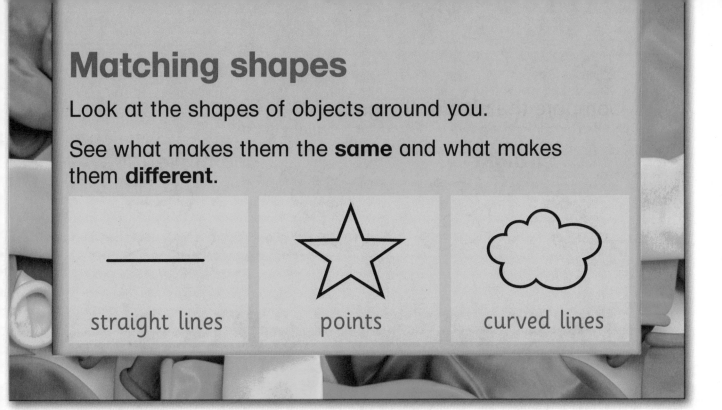

straight lines   points   curved lines

I Draw lines to join each rocket to its shadow.

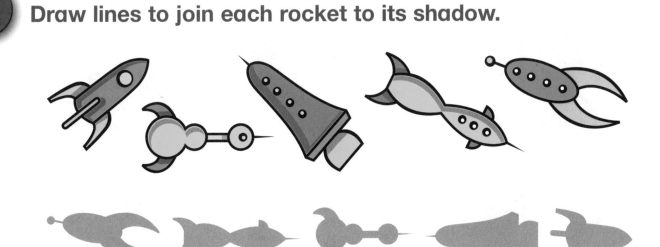

II Cross out the odd one in each row.

a

b

c

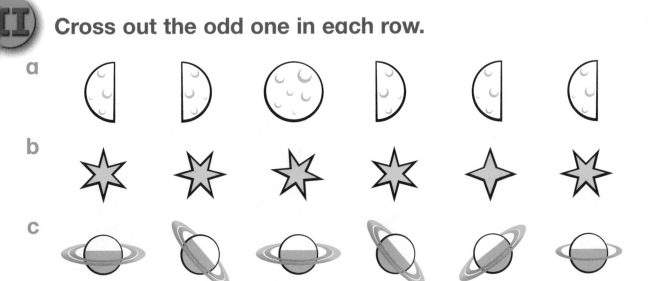

Comparing sizes

Compare the **size** of things.

smallest ➡ ➡ largest

I Tick the **largest** in each set. Cross out the **smallest** in each set.

a

b

c

d

e

f

II Draw lines to join these parcels in order of size. Start with the smallest.

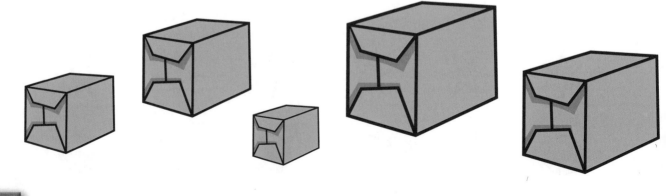

Numbers to 3

Talk about numbers **1**, **2** and **3**.

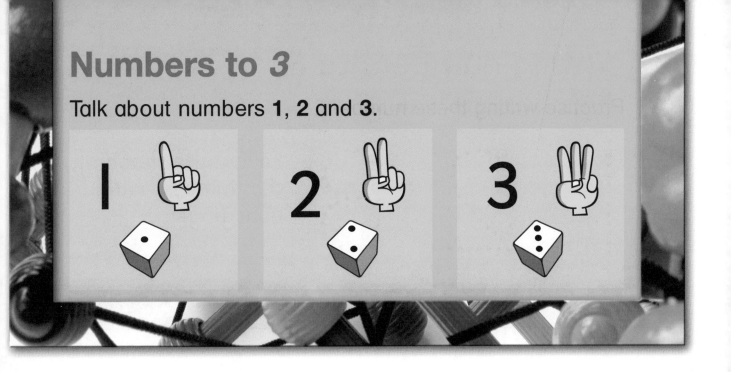

I Draw lines to join the numbers to their matching sets.

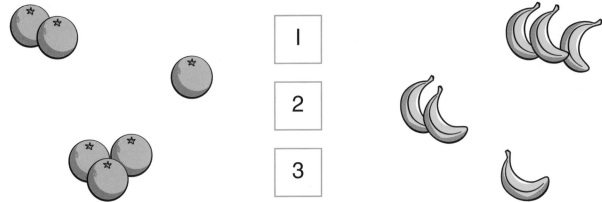

II Cross out the odd one in each set.

a

c

b

d

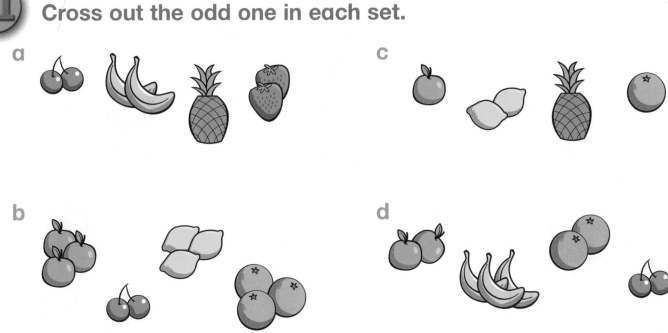

Writing numbers to *3*

Practise writing these numbers.

Follow the shape of the numbers with your finger.

I Write these numbers. Start at the red dots.

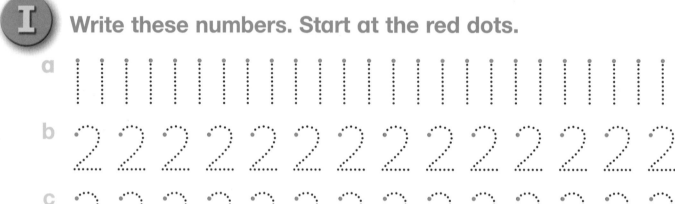

a

b

c

II Write the number on each card. Draw the same number of candles on each cake.

a

b

c

Recognising shapes

Look at the **shapes** of things around you.

I Find these shapes in the big picture. Colour them to match.

II Draw lines to join each lid to the correct box. Colour to match.

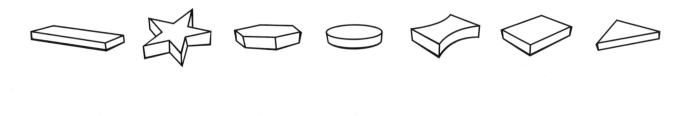

Comparing lengths

Compare the **lengths** of different objects.

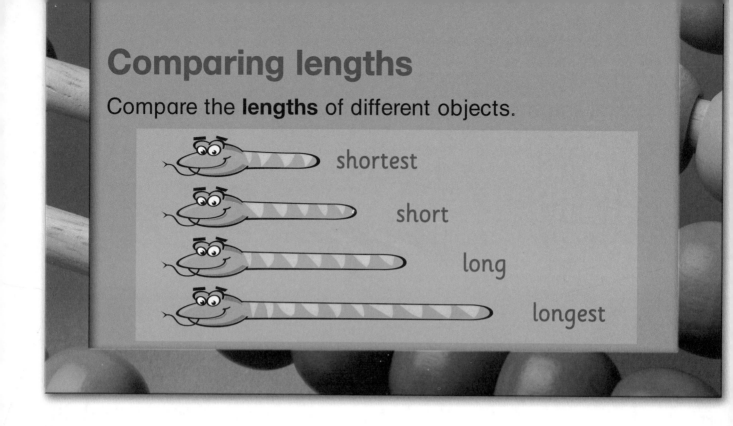

shortest

short

long

longest

I **Look at these objects.**

Circle the longest in each group.

Circle the shortest in each group.

a

b

c

d

II **Colour the longest scarf blue. Colour the shortest scarf red.**

a    b    c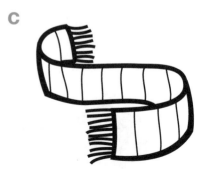

Numbers 4, 5 and 6

Talk about numbers **4**, **5** and **6**.

I Draw juggling balls to match the number below each clown.

a   b   c

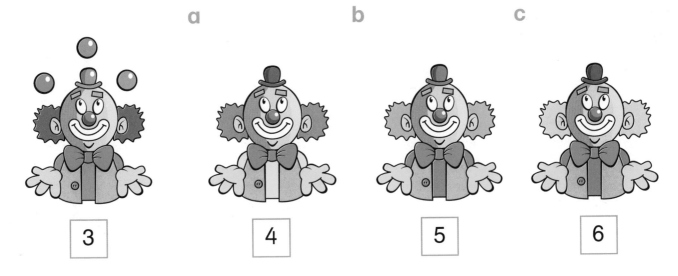

3   4   5   6

II Draw lines to join each card to the correct number.

4   5   6

Writing numbers to 6

Practise **writing** these numbers.

4	5	6
2 3 4	2 3 4 5	2 3 4 5 6

I Write these numbers. Start at the red dots.

a   4 4 4 4 4 4 4 4 4 4 4 4 4 4 4

b   5 5 5 5 5 5 5 5 5 5 5 5 5 5 5

c   6 6 6 6 6 6 6 6 6 6 6 6 6 6 6

II Write these numbers. Draw the same number of spots on each balloon.

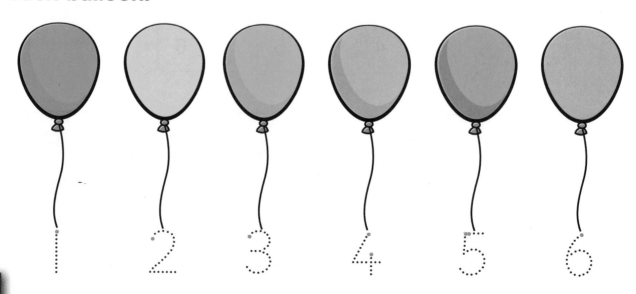

1   2   3   4   5   6

Counting to 5

When you count objects, the **last number** you say tells you how many there are.

 Draw lines to join the matching kites.

 Count each set of birds. Write down the number.

a    c    e

 b    d   f

Ordering events

We often do things in a certain **order**.

I Write the numbers 1, 2, 3 and 4 to show the order of each activity.

a
 ☐ ☐  ☐  ☐

b
 ☐ ☐ ☐  ☐

II Draw a line to show when you do these things.

| morning |

| afternoon |

| evening |

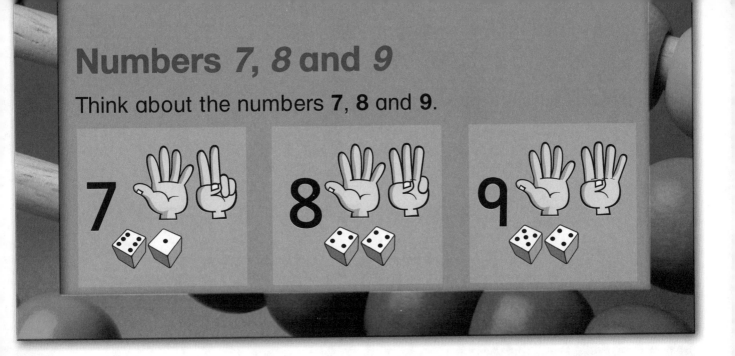

Numbers 7, 8 and 9

Think about the numbers 7, 8 and 9.

I Draw the right number of spots on each ladybird.

a

7

b

8

c

9

II Circle the odd one out in each row.

a

b

c

Writing numbers to 9

Practise **writing** these numbers.

7   1234567

8   12345678

9   123456789

I   **Write these numbers. Start at the red dots.**

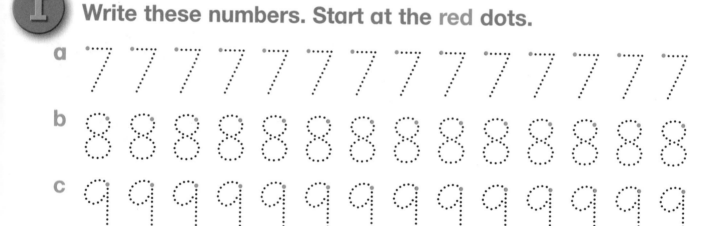

a   7 7 7 7 7 7 7 7 7 7 7 7 7 7

b   8 8 8 8 8 8 8 8 8 8 8 8 8 8

c   9 9 9 9 9 9 9 9 9 9 9 9 9 9

II   **Write the numbers. Colour the stars to match each number.**

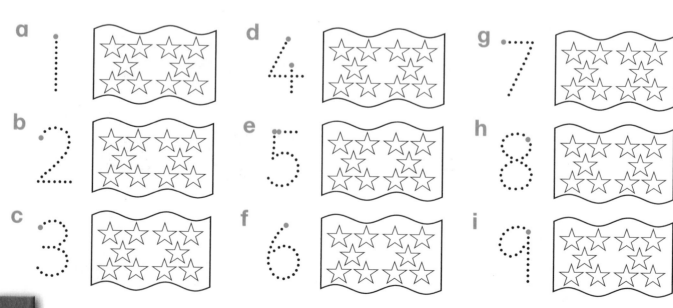

a 1   d 4   g 7

b 2   e 5   h 8

c 3   f 6   i 9

Patterns

Shapes and **colours** can make different patterns.

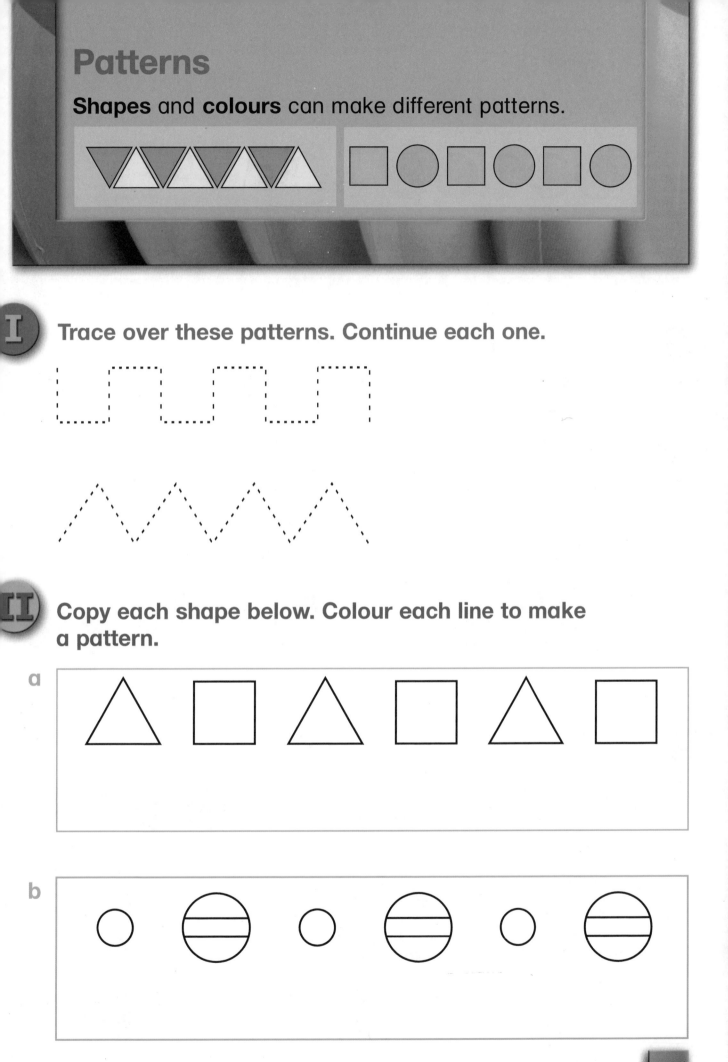

I Trace over these patterns. Continue each one.

II Copy each shape below. Colour each line to make a pattern.

a

b

Pennies

We count pennies to make **totals**.

5 pennies add together to make 5p.

I Count the pennies. Write the totals in each purse.

a

b

c

d

II Count each row of pennies. Colour the matching label.

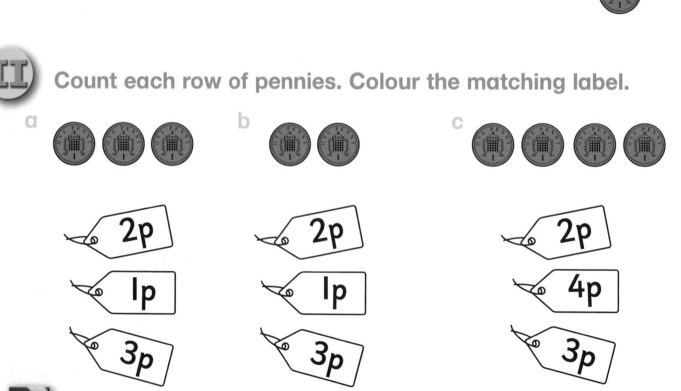

a

2p

1p

3p

b

2p

1p

3p

c

2p

4p

3p

Zero *0* and *10*

Practise writing **0** and **10**.

0 1 2 3 4 5 6 7 8 9 10

I Write over these numbers. Start at the red dots.

a O O O O O O O O O O O O O O

b 10 10 10 10 10 10 10 10 10

II Follow each path to join 0 and 10 to the correct fields of sheep.

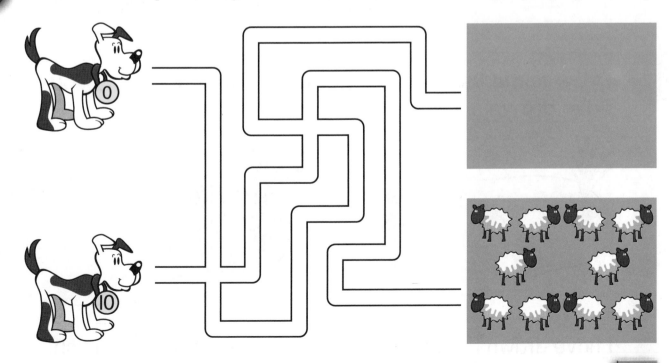

Counting to 10

Count the flowers and say the numbers out loud.

1 2 3 4 5 6 7 8 9 10

I   Draw lines to join each set of frogs to the correct number.

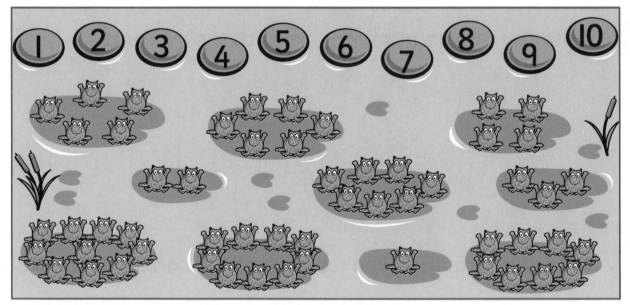

II   Draw some fish in these ponds. Count how many you have drawn.

a

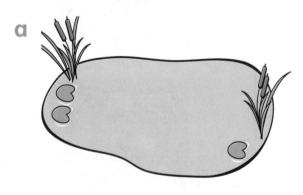

b

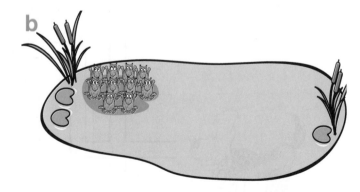

I have drawn ☐ fish.   I have drawn ☐ fish.

Recognising numbers

Try to learn these **numbers** and their **names**.

1   2   3   4   **5**   6   7   8   9   **10**

one   two   **three**   four   **five**   six   seven   eight   nine   **ten**

 Draw the correct number of spots on each kite.

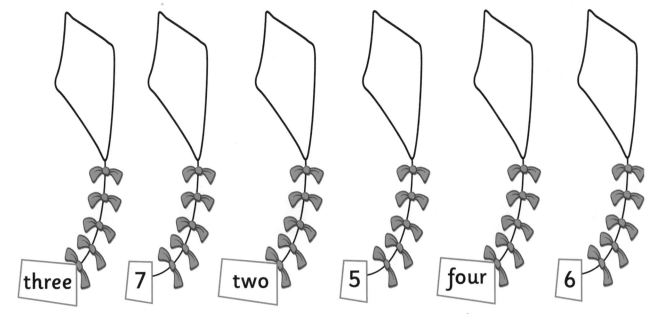

three   7   two   5   four   6

 Cross out the odd one on each line.

a

b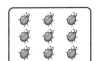

c

1 more

There is **1 more** ball in each row.

I Draw 1 more balloon in each group. Write how many balloons there are altogether.

a

☐

c

☐

b

☐

d

☐

II Draw one more candle on each cake. Complete the sentence.

a

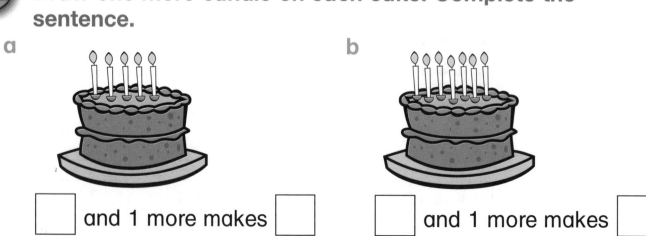

☐ and 1 more makes ☐

b

☐ and 1 more makes ☐

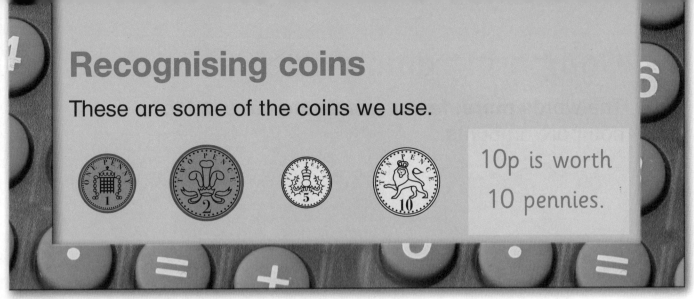

Recognising coins

These are some of the coins we use.

10p is worth
10 pennies.

I Cross out the odd one in each purse.

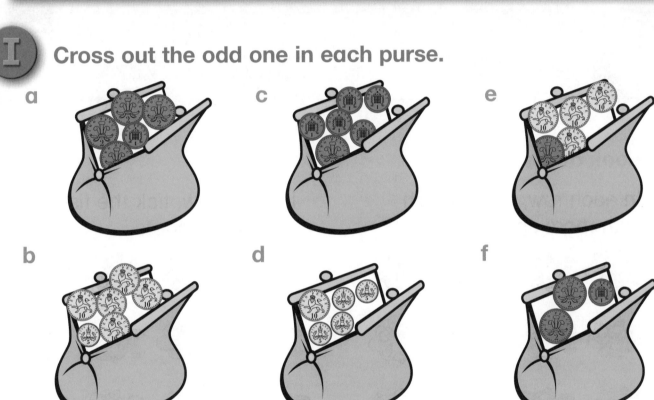

a

b

c

d

e

f

II Write the totals for each of these.

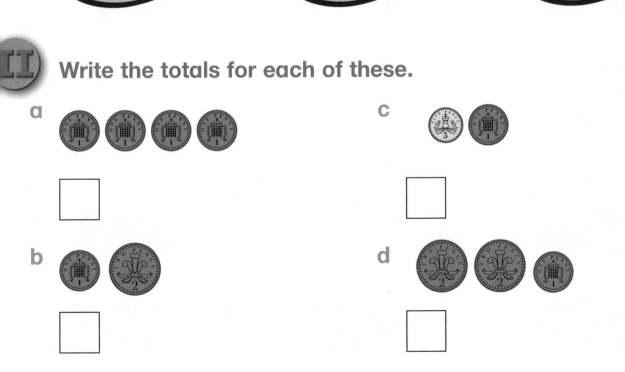

a

b

c

d

Comparing amounts

The words **more**, **fewer** and **same** are used to compare amounts.

- There are **more** blue fish than red fish.
- There are **fewer** red fish than yellow fish.
- There are the **same** number of blue fish as yellow fish.

I   **Look at the fish.**

a   In each row, tick the fish with **more** spots.

b   In each row, tick the fish with **fewer** spots.

II   **Look at each set of fish. Draw bubbles by the second fish.**

a   Draw **more** bubbles.

b   Draw **fewer** bubbles.

c   Draw the **same** number of bubbles.

Naming shapes

Try to learn the names of these shapes. Count the **number of sides** of each shape.

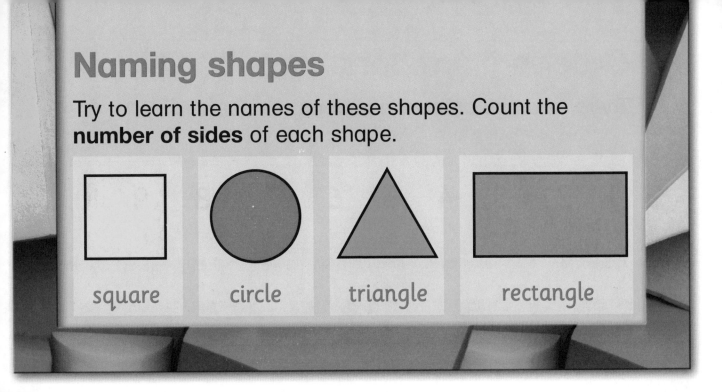

square   circle   triangle   rectangle

 Colour the shapes in the picture to match the colour of the shapes above.

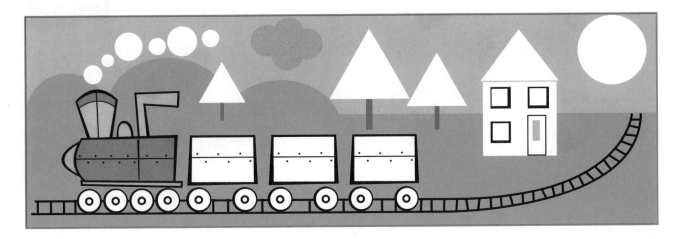

II Look at these shapes. Count the shapes.

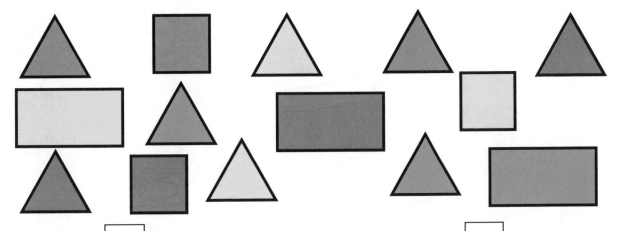

a There are ☐ 3-sided shapes.   b There are ☐ 4-sided shapes.

Ordering numbers

Try to learn the **order** of numbers.

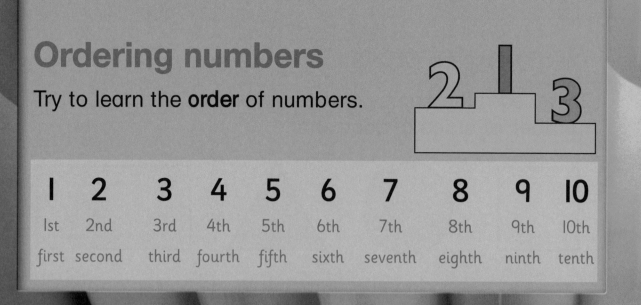

1	2	3	4	5	6	7	8	9	10
1st	2nd	3rd	4th	5th	6th	7th	8th	9th	10th
first	second	third	fourth	fifth	sixth	seventh	eighth	ninth	tenth

I Draw lines to join these in order.

a

b

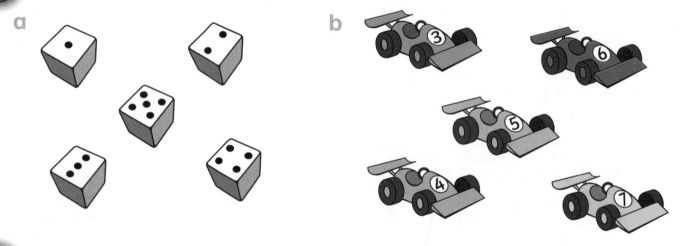

II These boats are in a race. Colour the 1st red. Colour the 2nd blue. Colour the 3rd yellow.

FINISH LINE

26

Finding totals

Count each set to find a total.

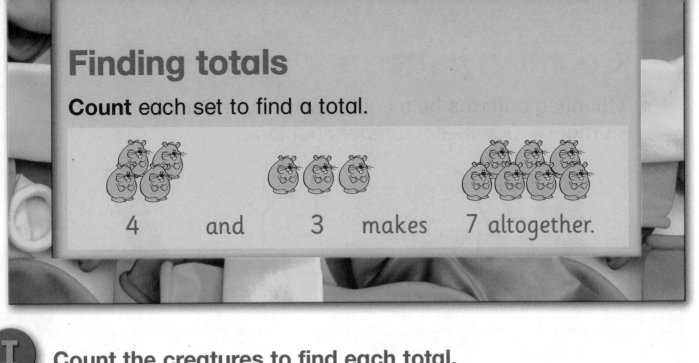

4   and   3   makes   7 altogether.

I Count the creatures to find each total.

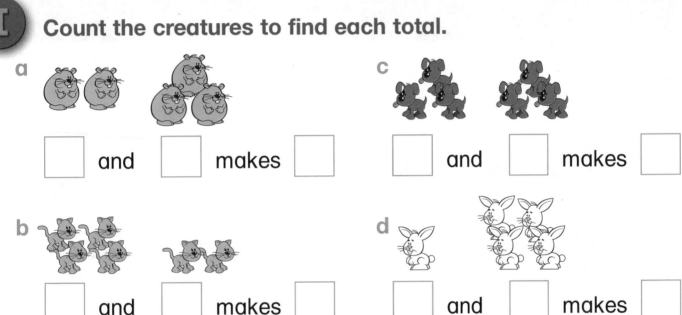

a ☐ and ☐ makes ☐

c ☐ and ☐ makes ☐

b ☐ and ☐ makes ☐

d ☐ and ☐ makes ☐

II Draw 3 more spots on each bear. How many are there now on each bear?

a There are ☐ spots on this bear.

b There are ☐ spots on this bear.

c There are ☐ spots on this bear.

Counting patterns

Counting patterns help you to work out **missing numbers**. Say these numbers out loud.

The missing numbers are 4 and 6.

I Write the missing numbers.

a   3 4 5 6 ☐ ☐ 9

b   10 9 8 7 ☐ ☐ ☐

c   5 6 7 8 ☐ 10 ☐

d   12 11 10 ☐ ☐ ☐ 6

II How far can you count past 10? Read these numbers and colour the ones you know.

6 7 8 9 10 11 12 13 14 15 16 17 18 19 20

Adding

You **add** things by putting them together and finding a **total**.

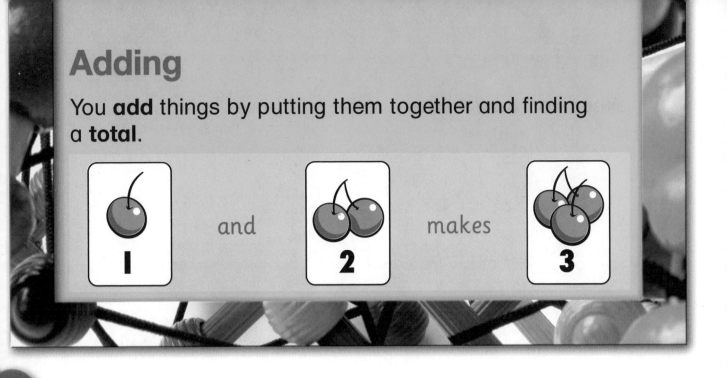

1   and   2   makes   3

I   **Write the missing numbers. Add them up.**

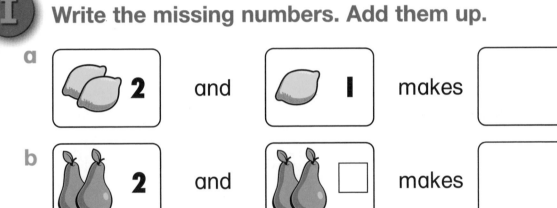

a   2   and   1   makes ☐

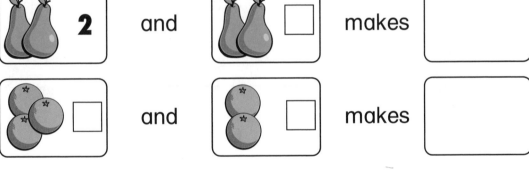

b   2   and   ☐   makes ☐

c   ☐   and   ☐   makes ☐

II   **Join together the dominoes with matching totals.**

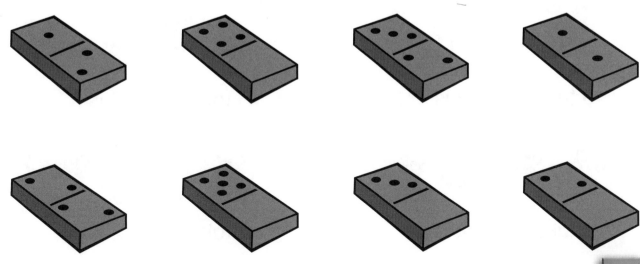

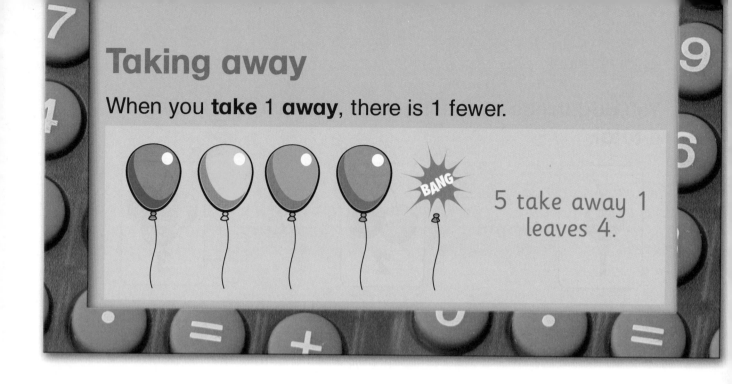

Taking away

When you **take** 1 **away**, there is 1 fewer.

5 take away 1
leaves 4.

I Cross 1 out and write what is left.

a

4 take away 1 is ☐

c

3 take away 1 is ☐

b

5 take away 1 is ☐

d

6 take away 1 is ☐

II Cross 2 out and write what is left.

a

3 take away 2 is ☐

c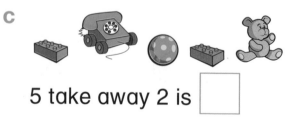

5 take away 2 is ☐

b

4 take away 2 is ☐

d

6 take away 2 is ☐

O'clock time

When the minute hand points to the 12 it shows an **o'clock** time.

The hour hand is pointing to 4.

This clock shows 4 o'clock or 4.00.

I Write these times.

a

[ ] o'clock

b

[ ] o'clock

c

[ ] o'clock

d

[ ] o'clock

e

[ ] o'clock

f

[ ] o'clock

II Join the clocks which show the same time.

7:00

2:00

5:00

ANSWERS

Page 2
I Check child's sorting.

II
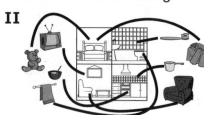

Page 3
I

II
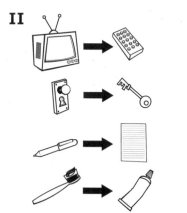

Page 4
I
a ⎍⎍⎍⎍   e ⌇⌇⌇⌇
b ⌒⌒⌒   f ∿∿∿
c ⋀⋀⋀   g ⌣⌣⌣
d ∼∼∼   h ⊓⊔⊓

II Check child's line pattern.

Page 5
I

II

Page 6
I
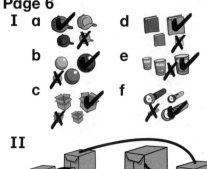

a   d
b   e
c   f

II
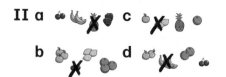

Page 7
I
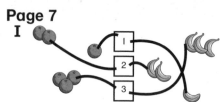

II a   c
b   d

Page 8
I
a ||||||||||||||||||
b 22222222222222
c 33333333333333

II
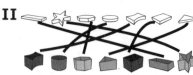

Page 9
I Check the shapes are coloured correctly.

II
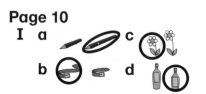

Page 10
I
a   c
b   d

II Check **a** is coloured blue and **b** is coloured red.

Page 11
I a   b   c
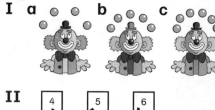

II
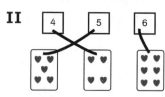

Page 12
I
a 44444444444444
b 55555555555555
c 66666666666666

II

1   2   3   4   5   6

Page 13
I

II a 4   c 3   e 5
b 1   d 2   f 4

Page 14
I a 3, 1, 4, 2
b 1, 3, 4, 2

II
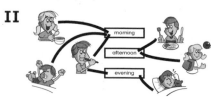

morning
afternoon
evening

Page 15
I a   b   c
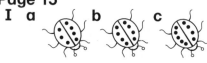

II a
b
c